By the same author:

MOTS D'HEURES, GOUSSES, RAMES

The Floriculturist's Vade-Mecum
of Exotic and Recondite Plants,
Shrubs and Grasses
and One Malignant Parasite

EN · LA · ROSE · JE · FLEURIE

The Floriculturist's Vade-Mecum of Exotic and Recondite Plants, Shrubs and Grasses and One Malignant Parasite

Written and Illustrated by
Luis d'Antin van Rooten

Doubleday & Company, Inc., Garden City, New York   1973

DESIGNED BY EARL TIDWELL

ISBN: 0-385-00900-3
Library of Congress Catalog Card Number 72-89356
Copyright © 1973 by Catharine Kelly van Rooten
All Rights Reserved
Printed in the United States of America
First Edition

To the memory of my mother who adored heliotropes and that of my mother-in-law whose family motto is: "En la rose je fleurie."

CONTENTS

FOREWORD

This modest monograph was inspired by sheer nostalgia. With advancing age, my childhood memories are highlighted by the remembrance of the flagrant, golden and ubiquitous SPITUNIA (*amphora salivaria*). It was sometimes called a GABOONIA (*amphora salivaria vulgaris*), but there is no discernible difference between the two. They are the same. The SPITUNIA is closely associated with the SALIVAS, such as SPUTUM (*saliva humana*), a universal ground cover, and the common NORTH-AMERICAN CHAW (*saliva nicotiana*). For this last a special taste must be acquired.

The onetime popularity of the SPITUNIA reached epic proportions. It was an inundation that saturated our whole social structure. An ideal pot plant, it was an indispensable item of interior decor. The SPITUNIA graced the Peacock Alley of the old Waldorf-Astoria in New York and the lobby of the St. Francis in San Francisco and the public rooms of every inn and hostelry in between. It was to be found in the most exclusive clubs. A photograph of the Great Hall at The Players in New York, circa 1907, features some outstanding specimens. It added dignity to the most humble saloons and poolrooms of our land.

The SPITUNIA found its place in the American home as a miniature French hybrid, the COUPES D'OR (*Microamphora salivaria gallica*), which, of course, we soon came to call "cuspidor." The French they are a funny race, and so are we. While they hybridize, we anglicize. The SPITUNIA was usually to be found on the hearth near Father's chair, with its side table, reading lamp, pipe-rack, and cigar humidor. A felicitous composition, the very spit and image of domestic comfort and tranquility.

In the '20s and '30s of the present century they rapidly disappeared, like my youth. Assiduous researchers may find a stray specimen here and there, but I am afraid its liquidation and eventual extinction are inevitable. I find it difficult to explain. Perhaps the profound changes we have experienced in our social mores were a contributing cause; or perhaps its blatant, brassy blooms do not harmonize with the sterile gloss of stainless steel and plastics of our modern interiors. The SPITUNIA required assiduous and daily care. It had to be drenched with water at frequent intervals or it would develop a trenchant and unpleasant aroma. This burden alone would be reason enough for floriculturists to abandon its cultivation. Who knows?

It is impossible to describe the vogue of the SPITUNIA to the younger generation. It is as unreal to them as the crash of '29 or the battle of Verdun. The SPITUNIA has taken its place in History along with Agincourt, Marathon and the Dodo. Alas! 'tis pity she's no more.

I have not included in this modest work the genera HOMOPHALLUS, CONVULVA and DECOITUS, despite the amazing specimens that have been observed and their great variety, simply because they are so common. Miss Laura Gaylord, of Westport, Connecticut, a skilled amateur gardener, once remarked of such scientific observation: "It's worse than wicked, it's vulgar." I am a broad-minded man, but I am in full accord with this Victorian dictum.

I hope this little volume with its rambling preamble will inspire other floriculturists to research and perhaps discover species I have overlooked. It will be a minor contribution to our ecology and an evaluation of our natural resources. It only requires a little time, effort, work, imagination and keeping your wit about you . . . Have fun!

Sears Point
Chatham, Massachusetts
1972

The Floriculturist's Vade-Mecum
of Exotic and Recondite Plants,
Shrubs and Grasses
and One Malignant Parasite

Decorative Plants and Flowers

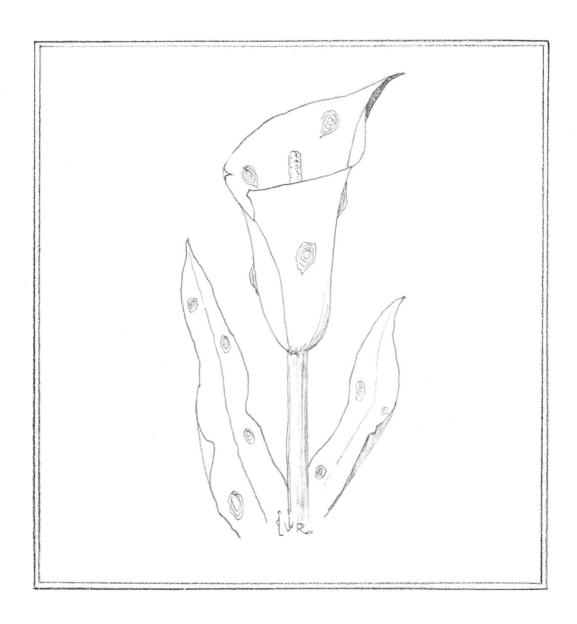

PLATE 1

THE CALLOUS LILY
epidermis indurata

A rare and exotic variety to add to your lily collection. It requires no special soil and thrives in full sun, semi-shade or shade. Ideal for naturalizing in a woodland. Its culture requires a great deal of manual work but the large pink to tan blooms, with their curious thick spots in their otherwise kid-glove smoothness, make them showpieces and well worth the effort. The mature lily wears its callouses as proudly as the gardener who raised them. Height 30″ to 3′-0″.

PLATE 2

TRANSITIVE VERBENA

grammatica fugitiva

This fragrant perennial seems to have only one object — to move. It seeds itself and will appear all over the garden, much like the so-called "showy marjoram." The gardener will want to uproot any unwanted specimens, but its gay, almost frivolous flowers brighten many a dull spot. If you want a more sedate and constant plant I suggest the INTRANSITIVE variety. It has one virtue: it will stay put.

PLATE 3

THE TRASH CANNA

detritus domesticus

The CANNA is one of our commonest and even vulgar flowers. It developed with our civilization, following the traces of the Iron Horse to the West, where it earned its nickname of the "Railroad Lily." Extremely hardy, flourishing in any soil or exposure, it was a great favorite with our grandparents as a space filler for otherwise impossible locations. The TRASH CANNA was usually placed on either side of the gate in the back fence and hence became known as the "Lily-of-the-Alley." It is impervious to insect pests and if properly treated at the nursery is even impervious to rust. In rural and suburban areas, skunks and raccoons may raise some hell with the CANNAS, but the damage can easily be repaired. After a few years the CANNAS may get a little battered and ratty-looking. Simply toss them aside and set up a new batch. The seedpod is rather interesting in form and I have included a specimen in my illustration. They need very little attention, although a thorough drenching on occasion may be advisable. Height 2'-6" to 3'-0".

PLATE 4
COLUMBARIUM
depositus cinereus

The Art of Landscape Architecture and garden planning was first practiced in this country by talented amateurs, such as George Washington at Mt. Vernon and Thomas Jefferson at Monticello and the campus of the University of Virginia, with its charming serpentine brick wall. Professionals such as Frederick Law Olmsted, Sr., (1822--1903) and Calvert Vaux (1824--1895) took over during the nineteenth century, producing among other works the layout of Central Park in New York City. The monumental tradition was carried on by Frederick Law Olmsted, Jr., and others into the present century. Their influence was felt in the design and general layout of our larger cemeteries, such as Arlington National Cemetery (attributed to Major L'Enfant), Forest Lawn in Glendale, California, and the oldest municipal cemetery in America, Mount Auburn, in Boston, Massachusetts. The superintendents of these and similar necropolises were devoted horticulturists and developed many new varieties and hybrids. As a member of the acting profession I derive a certain pride in having naturalized some primroses from Mount Auburn, final resting place of Edwin Booth, America's greatest actor and founder of The Players, a club of which I am honored to be a member. The primroses were presented to me by the daughter of a former superintendent of Mount Auburn.

All this preliminary discussion is necessary to any consideration of the COLUMBARIUM. It is a very large plant, far beyond the scope of the average garden or gardener. I include it here merely as a curiosity and recommend a visit to your local cemetery to admire the infinite variety of blooms it displays and the many ornate urns that are part and parcel of its "raison d'être." It is a monumental potting shed.

PLATE 5

THE GORGE ROSE
vomitus alimentarium

No rose garden is complete without at least one specimen of this sickly yellow rose, which seems to thrive on a sour or acid condition. Its distinguishing mark is a swelling in the neck of the stem, fibrous in nature and filled with an acrid liquid. Doesn't sound very attractive, does it? Still, at the turn of the century it was extremely popular, especially among literary people, who would use it in simile and metaphor, for example: "Desmond watched as his daughter passionately embraced the Oriental chauffeur. His gorge rose." Obviously his pet name for his beloved offspring. In those days nobody ever wrote novels about people who didn't have Oriental chauffeurs, either. If you can find a specimen, add it to your collection. It will be a conversation piece.

PLATE 6

CELIBACY
admajorem deigloriam

This lily-white flower so often found carved on the capitals and crockets of Gothic cathedrals is more of an ecclesiastical controversy than a botanical specimen. Dicta dating back to Pope St. Innocent I in A.D. 404 concerning its forced culture by the clergy are matters of historical record. Popes St. Leo I (440–461) and St. Gregory VII (1073–1085) must be included among its proponents, and the subject was discussed at length at the Consistories of Vienne (1311–1312), Constance (1414–1418) and Basel (1431–1449). Today, Pope Paul VI has expressed himself quite forcefully on this horticultural subject.

It is a humble flower of an almost incredible delicacy and purity. Today it is seldom found outside monastery, convent and parish-house gardens. It is closely allied to Virtue (q.v.). Many people doubt its existence, honest.

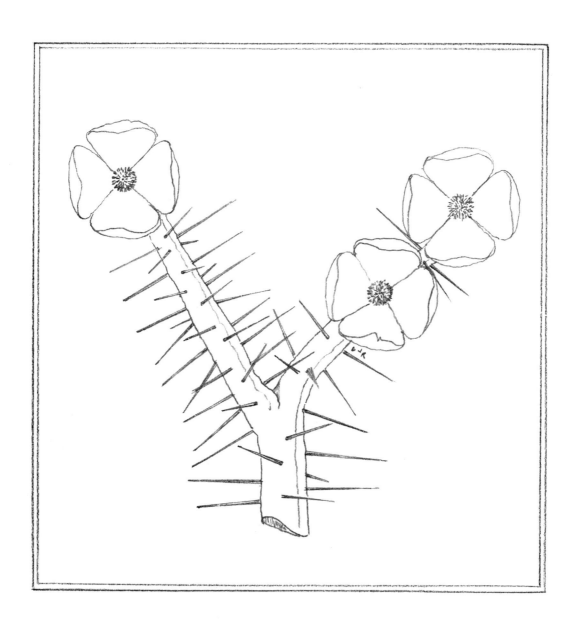

PLATE 7

JEEPERS CREEPERS

dictum bowdleriense

This succulent desert ground-vine, when first found in the desert by early Spanish explorers, was named "Jesus Christ's crown-of-thorns." Its one-inch spikes can inflict a painful puncture and inspire a call upon the Lord. Thomas Bowdler, English editor, who had the temerity to wash Shakespeare's mouth out with soap, as well as to expurgate Gibbon's *Decline and Fall of the Roman Empire*, thereby reducing it to readable length, extended his purifying influence to this humble desert growth. He renamed it in honor of a Yankee gold prospector, who is otherwise undistinguished, one Zachariah Q. Jeeper.

This creeper prefers a sandy soil, little water and much sun. Its blood-red blossom is quite beautiful when viewed in the mass. It can be grown as an annual in the temperate zones.

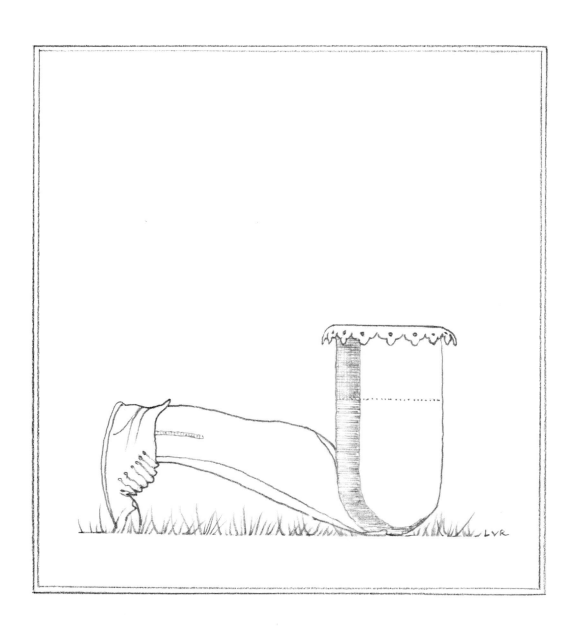

PLATE 8

HOUSEMAID'S KNEE

arthritis vulgaris

This modest flower, once quite common at the turn of the century, has virtually disappeared, one of the contributing causes being the fact that our Affluent Society cannot afford domestics. The culture of the plant requires an inordinate amount of work, more than the average gardener wants to devote to it. The blossom is large, light pink suffused with reddish tones. It is surprising to discover how many gardeners of retirement age, when in a nostalgic mood, would like to get their hands on one. Sic transit gloria mundi.

PLATE 9

LATE FLOWERING DINNER BELL
campanula prandialis tardis

This delightful night-flowering vine was introduced to the Hispanic colonies in America from the Iberian peninsula. The fact that the Spanish people eat quite late at night, around ten, coinciding with the opening of the first blooms of this plant, earned it its name. It has an appetizing odor, and many an evening meal is served al fresco under an arbor covered with the LATE FLOWERING DINNER BELL. The blooms are profuse and its perfume has a lingering quality and evokes nostalgic echoes of past repasts. It invites to prandial reunions and inspires conversation. It is a summons to make greater use of your garden and its products.

PLATE 10

DORBELS

alerta janitrix

DORBELS have been identified as the Elizabethan ALARUMS so often planted with HAUTBOYS, a red-flowered French importation. They are hardy, will grow in any soil, and require little attention. They have an extensive root system. The blossoms, when dried, will add an often surprising note in the house. A must for your dooryard planting. It can be quite electrifying.

PLATE 11

SHRINKING VIOLET

viola decrescens

The most modest of the violet family, the SHRINKING VIOLET clings to the soil, seldom over three inches high. At the slightest sign of exposure the blossoms will shrink into themselves, very much like the so-called SENSITIVE plant. Almost imperceptible in the garden, they possess unsuspected hidden qualities that can be brought out by careful cultivation. A spring flower, it dies down during the summer months. It proliferates by means of long shoots which take root, always seeking out sheltered nooks and crannies. It may surprise you by what it can do under heavy shrubbery if dealt with with gentleness and caution.

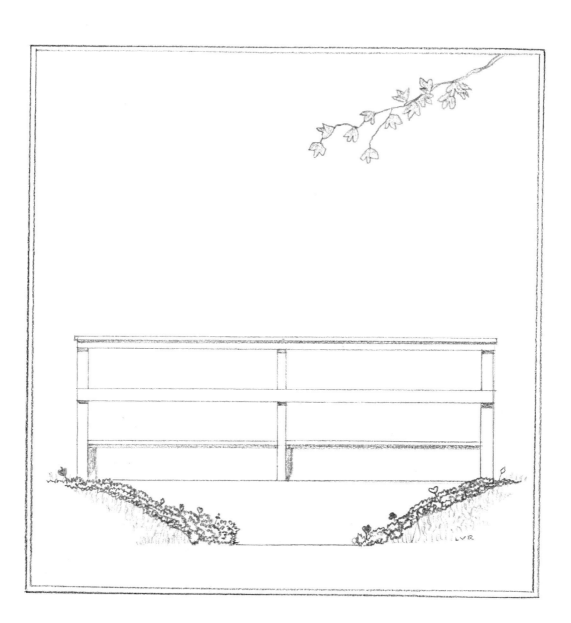

PLATE 12

TRUMP
charta triumphalis

TRUMP is one of the most controversial plants in the gardener's compendium. Professional and expert amateurs can seldom agree on anything about it except its suitability. If you are fortunate enough to have a brook or stream crossing your property, then a bridge is essential. The abutments and foundations can be hidden and covered with TRUMP. Values vary according to locale and it is best to select your TRUMP by competitive bids. It will hold the soil, guard your banks and facilitate crossing from one side to the other. TRUMP is at its best when the crossing is rough. It is advisable, once TRUMP is established, to thin it out, but there are circumstances when this method of culture is totally inadvisable. This is a point on which experts can easily and often disagree. In any case the ground should be well spaded, really put your heart in it, and by all means join a garden club. They are generally diamonds in the rough. Some gardeners prefer their bridge with no TRUMP at all.* This requires considerable skill and finesse for a successful result. In any case, TRUMP is a good cover, and holds the soil well with little care. It is a rapid grower, often being doubled in short order, and sometimes redoubled, one reason why experts will tell you to count and keep track of your TRUMP. It can almost be called a game. Here is a tried and true adage: when in doubt, use TRUMP.

* Ibid. four hearts.

PLATE 13

STENO

puella officinalis

Here is the ideal pot plant for office decoration. It is an indispensable item for the outer office, an attractive specimen adding much to a first impression. Started in pools, it is placed in its final container when fully trained and matured. It should be used in the private office with great restraint and discretion. Corresponding in the reception room, it can too easily become a co-respondent in the intimacy of a private office, a consummation devoutly to be avoided. Although they are on occasion heavy feeders, they can take care of themselves, so you don't have to worry about them over long holiday weekends. Some floriculturists claim that you should speak to your plants. A kind word now and then to a STENO might not do any good, but anyway it wouldn't hurt.

PLATE 14

HALCYON DAYSY

dies serenus

We have to go back to Greek mythology to find the origin of this delightful wildflower. Halcyone was the daughter of Aeolus and the wife of Ceyx. This latter decided to consult the oracle of Apollo, and his wife swore to keep vigil on a high bluff until his return. For weeks she spent her days scanning the horizon for the sail of her husband's ship, till the morning when his drowned form was washed ashore at her feet. With a cry of despair she leaped into the void. The gods, out of pity, changed them into kingfishers, doomed to spend their lives over the sea. Tradition tells us that they breed and nest at sea, and Zeus commanded that the seven days before and after the winter solstice when the kingfisher is nesting, be days of cloudless skies, calm seas and balmy breezes: the halcyon days. All accounts, however, fail to mention a very important fact: on the spot where Halcyone had stood, the HALCYON DAYSY sprang from the soil. It is considered a weed by most seed-growers and nurseries, so you have to find them yourself and gather the seeds. If you are fortunate enough to have a meadow on the water front, scatter the seeds you have gathered, in the spring, and come the halcyon days, you will have a field dotted with HALCYON DAYSIES, their faces ever turned seaward . . .

PLATE 15

FORWORT

semper prorsum

FORWORT is the ground cover par excellence. A low, thick, furze-like plant, it has only one drawback—it spreads only in one direction. Planted at the base of a fence, it will quickly grow out and cover any width of bed you desire. An edge trimmer will keep it within such bounds as you may wish. For a central bed, we recommend that you plant two clumps of FORWORT in the center with two clumps of BACKWORT (*semper retrus*). This latter spreads in the opposite direction from the FORWORT. In this way you can cover the area desired in half the time it would take to plant either one along just one edge. It requires no special soil, and trimming merely thickens the growth. The blooms are of no great interest but just keep coming and going. A conversation piece.

PLATE 16

RUCKUS

tumultus subitus

If you have a dull or empty space in your garden, let me recommend that you raise a RUCKUS. Its spike-like twisted twigs, quaking foliage and riotous bloom will enliven any too-quiet corner. Just plant the seeds and it will grow by itself. It is not a plant for conservative gardeners.

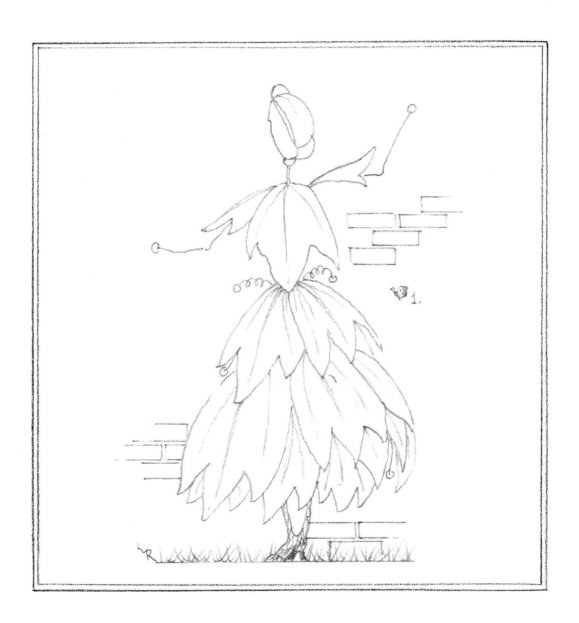

1.

PLATE 17

WALLFLOWER
infanta timida

This is a decorative plant that does best against a wall, having tendrils with suction cups that make it cling to masonry. Many gardeners refer to it as CLINGING VINE for this reason. Its lackluster foliage and insipid blooms seem an almost deliberate attempt on its part to make itself inconspicuous. It does have its virtues, nonetheless, too many perhaps for its own good, for many gardeners avoid it as too uninteresting and thereby doom it to oblivion. Somehow, like the poor, they are always with us. They prefer to be left undisturbed, but assiduous attention may bring out unexpected qualities and a certain old-fashioned charm. The WALLFLOWER is mainly useful to fill in bare spaces on your garden wall and to form a background contrast to the more showy blooms.

Also shown (1) is the microscopic butterfly, the MEXICAN BALD MINUTE TAPIOCA (*papilio chihuahensis*).

PLATE 18

TARNATION

condemnatio perpetuum

The white TARNATION is the traditional boutonniere for a groom, possibly as a symbol of the state he is entering. The groomsmen usually wear red TARNATIONS as a warning, which few of them seem to heed. Well, to paraphrase one of our foremost Philosophers of Folly, "What you seeds, is what you gets."

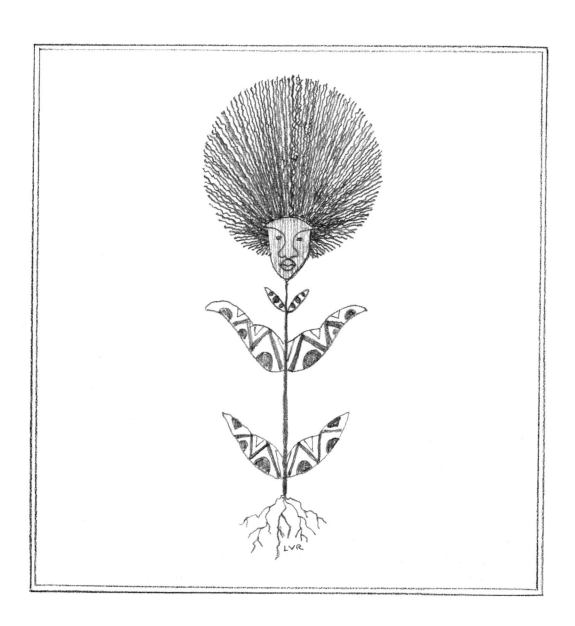

PLATE 19

TRUE LOVE'S-HAIR

capillus Nigeris

For centuries horticulturists have been trying to produce a pure black flower. The plot of Alexandre Dumas' novel *The Black Tulip* revolves about this problem. The best results have been blooms a deep purplish black and yet no one seemed to notice the *capillus Nigeris* introduced from Africa by the Phoenicians, because it was right under foot. It blended into the landscape and was simply taken for granted. It was finally recognized and classified by Rodney Howard True (1866–1940), Professor of Botany and Director of the Botanic Garden at the University of Pennsylvania, or, at least, attributed to him. In recent years great interest has been aroused in its proper culture and cultivation and there is no valid reason why it shouldn't take its rightful place among the other blooms that grace American gardens. There is an old ballad about it.

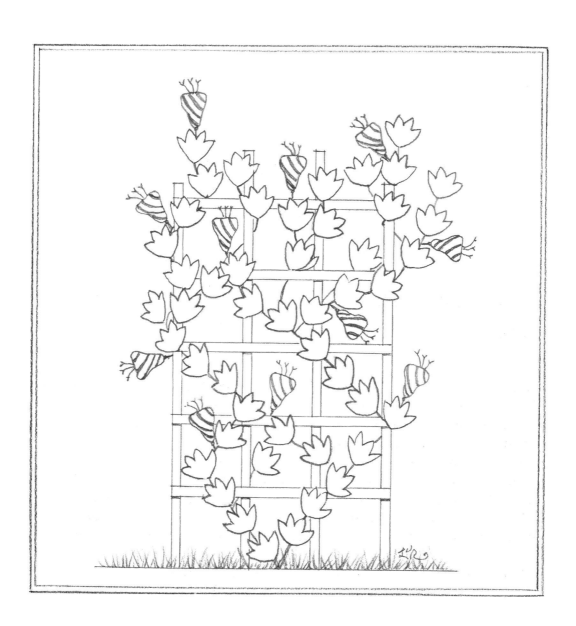

Plate 20

HISTERIA VINE
vinca histerica

This vine is best started in a slight depression, although it may break out spontaneously almost anywhere. Its growth is unpredictable and spasmodic. It may remain dormant for long periods and then suddenly break out with dazzling violence. Its bilious green foliage and angry yellow and violent purple striped trumpets make it an attention getter in any location. I suggest that it not be used in a small space. Its rampant growth can become uncontrollable and it will take over the less riotous bloomers. I am convinced that the current figure of speech, "climbing the walls," can be attributed to the outstanding propensity of the HISTERIA VINE. The seed packets should be marked "Use with caution."

PLATE 21

BLUE FUNK

tristitia glauca

The BLUE FUNK was called to my attention by Mr. Walter Bradbury, of New York City, a true seeker of the recondite. If you are in despair about some sunless corner of your garden, here is the perfect solution. The BLUE FUNK, a cousin of the FUNKIAS or HOSTAS, not only prefers shade, but actually seeks the solitude of a dark corner. It blooms best on a dismal and overcast day. Its deep blue flower could easily be substituted for the purple of mourning. Set out the corms under the shrubbery in the darkest corner you can find and then leave it alone. The BLUE FUNK prefers it that way.

PLATE 22

DUBIOSITY

spiritus ambiguus

Because of the undecided political situation in Africa it is doubtful that bulbs of this delightful flower can be obtained at this time. It is quite temperamental and will do well in acid or sweet soil, according to its inclination, or it may not burgeon at all. If you are successful in finding some DUBIOSITY bulbs you will be delighted with its variety of tints and shades and the slightly blurred markings of its petals. Some floriculturists admire it and others do not; the great majority are undecided. To my knowledge, no one has ever expressed a really definite opinion about it pro or con. There is even some controversy about its true origin: some say Africa and some say Asia. The only sure thing is, "Who knows?"

Shrubs and Dwarf Trees

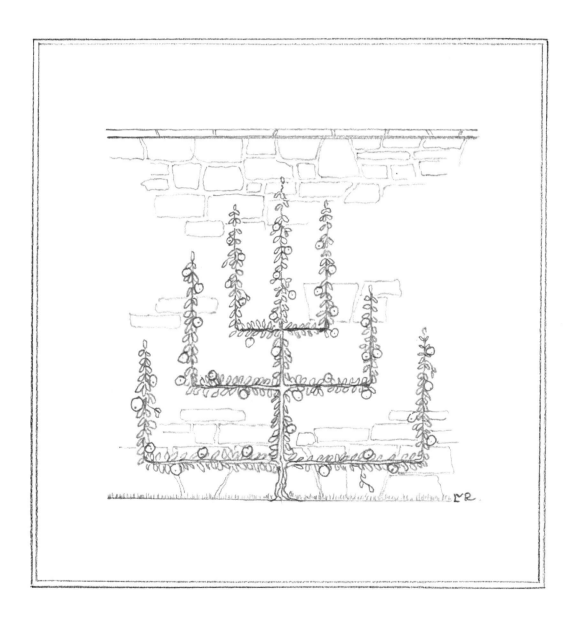

PLATE 23

ESPRIT DE L'ESPALIER
ingenium postfactum

This is not an individual specimen, but a variety grown in a specific way. If your garden is enclosed by a masonry wall, you plant fruit trees at the base and then train them into a formal shape. You must, of course, choose a sunlit wall and the reflected warmth will ripen the fruit more evenly. It takes a great deal of stapling and pruning and several years before the desired result is obtained. The fruit will be delicious. The only trouble is that you usually think of something more apropos than what you have planted, when it is too late to do anything about it.

PLATE 24

ST. JOSEPH'S PLUMB

plumbus lignarius

The Apocrypha tells us that when a spouse was sought for the Virgin Mary, all the eligible bachelors of the House of David were called together. Among them was Joseph, an elderly carpenter, and the staff he carried burst into bloom. This was accepted as a sign of divine approval and Joseph and Mary were wed. Both Matthew and Luke take the story on from there. The staff Joseph carried was the trunk of the dwarf *plumbus lignarius*. If you need a vertical accent in your garden, this is it. It grows as straight as the pines of the Bois de la Cambre, outside Brussels, which are used exclusively for telephone poles. The St. Joseph's Plumb is strictly decorative, in every sense of the word. The fruit is inedible, being extremely hard and having a strong metallic taste. It is impervious to insects but may be affected by rust. This can easily be controlled. Because of its association with St. Joseph, the fruit has become the trade symbol of carpenters and builders. Culture is easy, any soil will do. Very hardy.

PLATE 25

SAND BEECH

arena arena

The SAND BEECH thrives on all our ocean shores, alternating with STRAND (*ora calculis abundans*) and ROCKBOUND (*ora saxea*). It is one of Nature's most generous gifts to man and is to be thoroughly enjoyed in its great variety of textures and the many maritime curiosities the tides bring in to its stretches. Its greatest enemy is man himself, who vandalizes and covers it with garbage and cast-off rubbish. Remember, the beauty you spoil is everybody's.

PLATE 26

TIT WILLOW
mamilla japonica

About the time that James McNeill Whistler and the Impressionists were discovering the beauties and techniques of Hiroshige and Hokusai, Gilbert and Sullivan called the attention of Occidental civilization to the TIT WILLOW in a plaintive little ballad in one of their famous operettas. We know the Japanese as a diminutive people with small but skillful hands, dedicated to meticulous and minuscule works of Art and Craft. Their great contributions to Botany, in the development of Flower Arrangement, the hybridization of chrysanthemums and the development of dwarf trees, need no elaboration here. The TIT WILLOW is one of the rarest specimens in the art of bonsai, or dwarf trees. It takes several generations to bring one to perfection, but the result warrants the time. At maturity the TIT WILLOW bears a pair of seeds, ivory-colored and looking good enough to eat, but it's a "mustn't touch." If you want to leave your great-grand-children a rare inheritance, forget those ten shares of Standard Oil of New Jersey; instead study the Bonze philosophy, plant a TIT WILLOW and Banzai! bonsai.

Edible Plants and Herbs

PLATE 27

EASTERN STANDARD THYME
tempus invernale

There is hardly a recipe in the lexicon of fine cuisine that does not call for a pinch of thyme. In order to have fresh thyme on hand, some EASTERN STANDARD THYME should be started in pots in the fall for winter use. In the spring, DAYLIGHT SAVING THYME (*tempus aestivus*) should be planted, preferably in sandy, well-drained soil, in full sun. This will provide an adequate supply until late fall, when it will die down. It may, of course, be dried for winter use, but it is not quite the same as having a pot or so of fresh EASTERN STANDARD on the kitchen window-sill. DAYLIGHT SAVING THYME is a perennial and will come up in the spring from the previous year's planting. Always be sparing in your use of thyme. As the old saying has it, thyme is money.

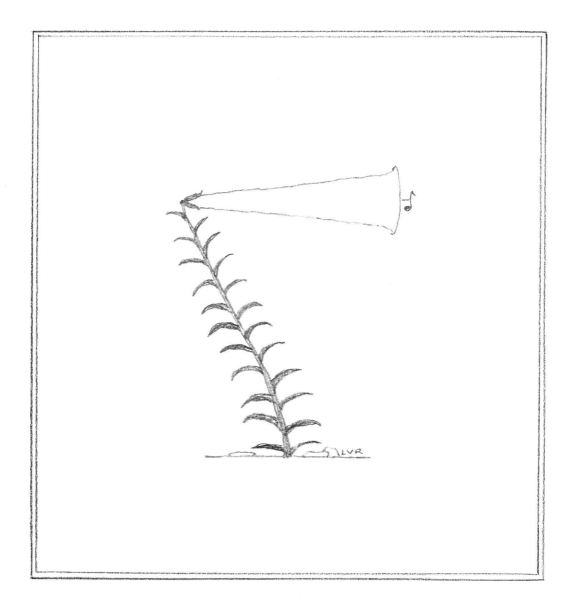

PLATE 28

ANGEL'S CRUMPET

panis angelicus

A golden yellow flower, the ANGEL'S CRUMPET is eminently edible if an old Aztec recipe is followed. Pick the fresh flowers, remove the pistils and stamen and wash clean of pollen. Dip the flowers in an egg-and-flour batter and fry in deep fat. They're simply heavenly. The modern Mexicans treat squash blossoms in this manner and they are what Madison Avenue would call a new taste thrill. The English insist on serving CRUMPETS with tea. De gustibus et coloribus non est disputandum.

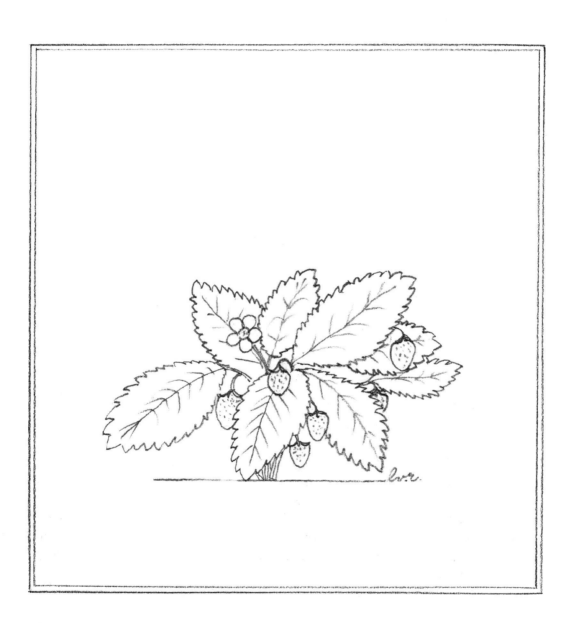

PLATE 29

PHRASE DEBOIT or MERDE

dictum cambronniense

According to legend, a peg-legged Gaul named Jambix Deboit, while hunting for truffles near his native village of Podevin, stumbled over an oak-tree root and fell headlong into a wild berry patch. He picked himself up, muttering, "Merde, alors," and ever since then these luscious berries were called MERDE. That is, until Mr. Bowdler came along and decided to do the same service to the French language that he had had the temerity to do to English and with pedantic accuracy renamed them PHRASE DEBOIT. At the battle of Waterloo, a square of the Imperial Guard was being cut to pieces by Wellington's English regulars and their commanding officer called out, "Where do you stand?" One version of the story has General Pierre Cambronne answering, "The Old Guard never surrenders, it dies." The more popular version states that Cambronne took the question literally and, looking down, found himself up to his ankles in wild berries and matter-of-factly replied, "Merde!" This more popular version inspired their Botanical classification, attributed to Charles Darwin. Whatever you call them, there is nothing like them in a bowl of clotted cream. In the French theater, on opening nights, there is a strange custom, dating back to the bohemian days of the wandering minstrels. The actors visit each other's dressing rooms and say, "Merde," probably meaning, "Tonight we eat."

PLATE 30

MINT JULIP

hospitalis septemptrionalis

The MINT JULIP is used to make a concoction highly popular in our Southern states. Its preparation is a ritual. In a tall silver glass (about twelve ounces) place a few leaves of MINT JULIP. With a wood muddler crush the leaves with a lump of sugar. Then fill the glass with finely crushed ice, being careful not to get any on the outside of the glass. Then fill the interstices with the finest Bourbon whiskey you can afford. You may decorate the whole with a few sprigs of MINT JULIP sprinkled with confectioners' sugar. This latter is pure "chichi." If the South really gave birth to the blues, they certainly provided the right antidote. You must, however, limit them to two to a guest, or you risk losing him.

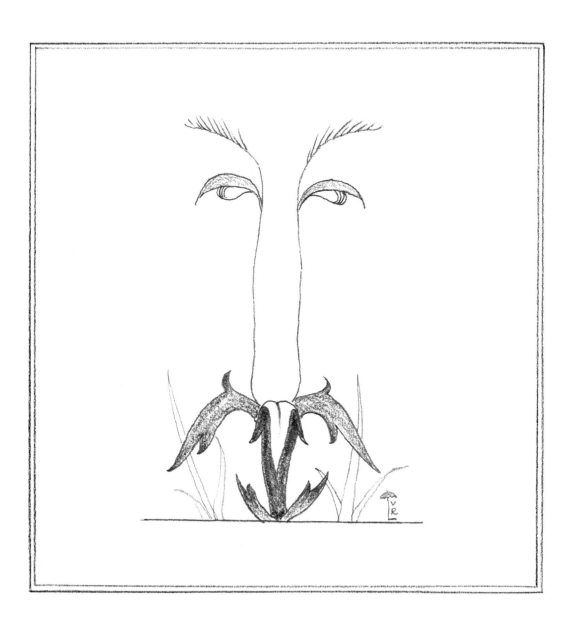

PLATE 31

UMBRAGE or MOUNTAIN PIQUE
herba obscura

This mountain herb, of medicinal properties, has a dark look about it, hence its Latin classification. Brew the leaves into a tea, and when you feel insulted by life, at odds with the world, take UMBRAGE. The effect may be quite disconcerting but effective.

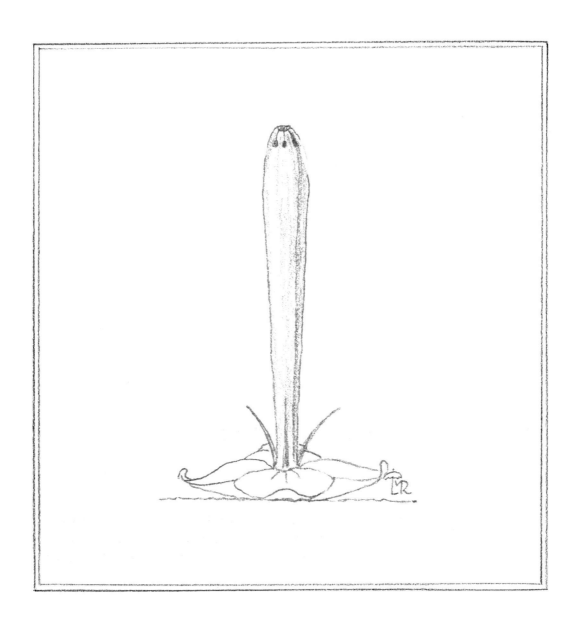

PLATE 32

LAVAGE

lavandula saponaria

LAVAGE is of the lavender family, but its roots possess a saponaceous quality common to a great variety of soapy plants. It is strictly a medicinal herb used as a detergent. It is a specific for disturbances of the large and semi-colon. A few individuals use it in salads to cut the sharpness of vinegar. I don't recommend it.

PLATE 33

COMMON SENSE
cumgrano salis

Whether you are planning a formal garden or striving for an informal natu-
ralistic effect, you need a common motif to bind the different elements together
into a unified and logical whole. For this purpose our Founding Fathers used
an old-fashioned herb called COMMON SENSE, a more sophisticated and delicate
variety of HORSE SENSE (*sensus equus*). Used as a hedge or trimmed border, or
as a focal point in such gardens as the one of the Governor's Palace in Wil-
liamsburg, Virginia, it was a taken-for-granted necessity of colonial life. A
decoction of its leaves was served in the coffeehouses of the day as a concomi-
tant to good conversation, relaxing the mind and liberating thought and
imagination. Using it as a simile, Thomas Paine wrote a brilliant political essay
(1776) that sold over a hundred thousand copies in its day. A nice mark for any
author to shoot at. It is a great pity that COMMON SENSE has become a rarity
in our gardens and our complex society. It is not easy to come by, but very
rewarding when it is found. Best if grown from seed, well nourished and
pruned to hold its shape.

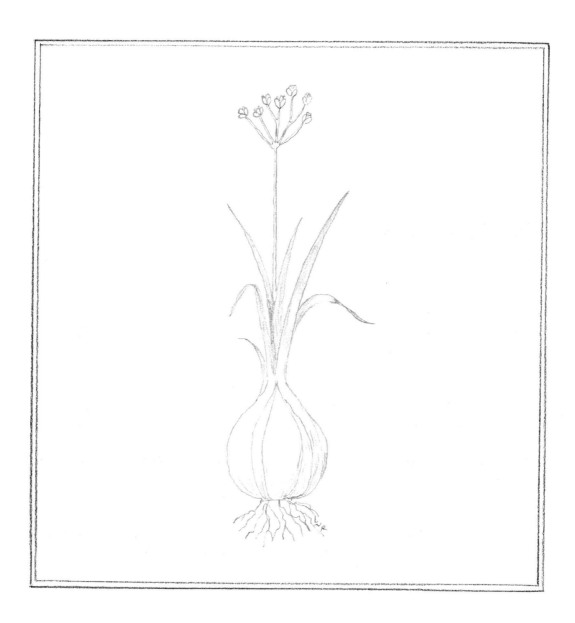

PLATE 34

GALLIC

condimentum mundiale

From the heights of the snow line of the Himalayas to the depths of the African and South American jungles, the wild GALLIC can be found. There is no doubt that prehistoric man rubbed his clay bowl with it before he poured in his dinosaur stew. References to GALLIC can be found in the earliest Egyptian and Babylonian hieroglyphs, as well as to its domesticated cousin the BUNION (*pedis pollex tumidus*). GALLIC was a basic condiment, to varying degrees, in universal cooking but was given its present name when Julius Caesar divided Gaul into three parts and introduced GALLIC to Rome. Both Calvin and Luther must have assumed that since it was so good it must be sinful, since all their followers and descendants, the WASPs, the most maligned of American minorities, eschewed the pungent bulb. They considered GALLIC to be fit only for "wops," "polacks," "litvaks" and "greasers." After World War I, doughboys returning from the trenches of France and Flanders raised the ostracized GALLIC to the point of gustatory acceptance in the United States. Today Americans of all classes and persuasions answer the cheerful cry of "Soup's On!" of GALLIC.

PLATE 35

GERRYMANDER

locus divisus

Elbridge Gerry (1744–1814) was twice elected Governor of Massachusetts. As Governor he interested himself in the natural potentials of his state and discovered that the Gerrymander proliferated there. He was aided in his researches by Gilbert Stuart (1755–1828), famed as much as a gourmet as a painter. GERRYMANDER had been known in England for a long time. In 1504 William Turner wrote that "taken out of measure" it "taketh men's wyttes." Of the GERRYMANDER only the seeds, growing in umbels, are used. They have a sweetish pleasant taste and are often blended with ground cuminseed. It is considered a specific for internal disorders and, when green, both the plant and seed have a disagreeable odor. One thing for sure is that it has been for many years a matter of great controversy. One might say, a seed of discontent.

PLATE 36

FETICH or FETISH

idolum falsum

FETICH is a root plant of simple foliage and like the mandrake it has a bifurcated root. The root, dried and ground to a fine powder, has been an ingredient of medicinal and magical potions since time immemorial. It is believed that the Druids used it much as the Mexican indigenes used Peyotl. Witch doctors of almost all primitive societies were familiar with it and used it as part of the contents of the small bags to be worn around the neck by their patients. Modern psychopathologists attribute certain erotic qualities to a FETICH. If this theory can be proven, then FETICH is one of the few true aphrodisiacs known to mankind.

PLATE 37

EASTEREG

ovum paschale

A must for the spring garden, the EASTEREG is the first fruit of the year to ripen. A smallish shrub, of inconsequential foliage and bloom, its multicolored fruit forms its main attraction. From time immemorial it has been the symbol of Spring Fertility Rites. Shaped somewhat like a nutmeg, though several times larger, it is a natural and inexplicable phenomenon in that one can predict its day of perfect ripeness, much as solar and lunar eclipses can be foreseen by astronomers. It will be ripe exactly forty days after the first appearance of MARDI GRASS. This latter is the reason for great rejoicing and spring festivals, particularly among communities of French Catholic origin, which explains why we affect the French pronunciation and call it "MARDIGRAH." In Slavic countries, suffering from long and cold winters, the Rites of Spring have a peculiar significance and they have developed hybrids of the EASTEREG with really remarkable coloring and patterns. If there still exists a Polish or Ukrainian neighborhood in your town, you may be able to obtain some beautiful specimens in the shops. To emphasize the importance of the EASTEREG in Slavic culture, I need only call to your attention the magnificent replicas in gold, jewels and rare enamels made by Fabergé for the Russian Imperial family and their court. American farmers use the EASTEREG as a calendar for letting poultry out of their winter coops to run free in the farmyard or wired runs and hence call it hen-fruit.

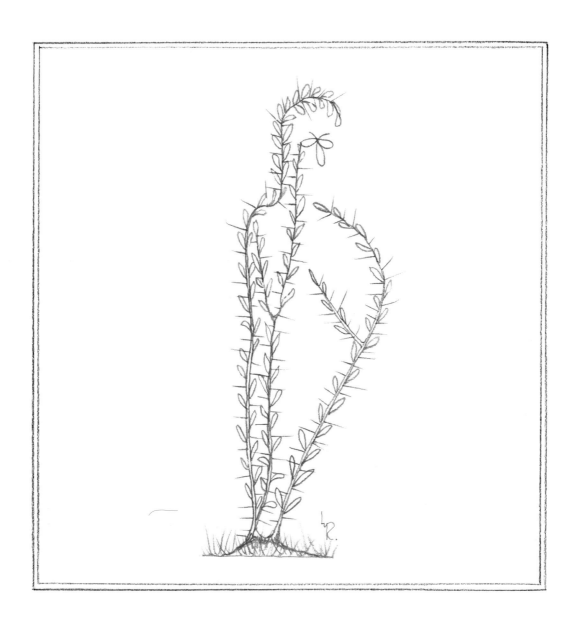

PLATE 38

HIGH DUDGEON
indignatio sublimis

A bitter and very thorny herb, it is the principal ingredient of an ointment celebrated in an old American folk song and will cure "corns, cramps, colick, chaps, tetters and chilblains." It is famed for its tonic qualities in all the Old Wives' pharmacopoeias. It tastes so awful, it must be good for you. At any rate, it is a relief just to get it down. A handful of HIGH DUDGEON leaves steeped in wine for several days is all the preparation needed. The dosage is two teaspoons every two hours until you begin to like it. Like castor oil it is habit-forming. Don't indulge too often as it tends to heighten the blood pressure and some cases of coronary and neurotic effects have been known in those who are over-indulgent in its use. It does clarify a curious line of Sir Walter Scott's: "I drink to thee in dudgeon and hostility."

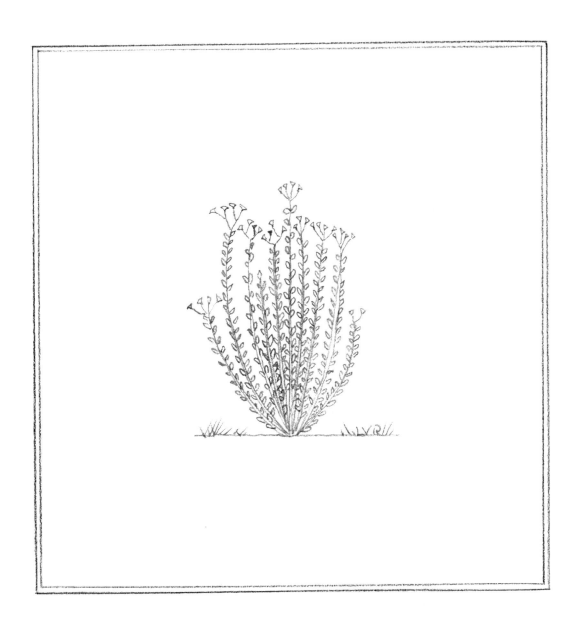

PLATE 39

RUE DE LA PAIX
iter elegans

RUE DE LA PAIX is an old French refinement of our COMMON RUE (*ruta graveolans*). A bitter herb, its medicinal qualities have been known from very early times. Hippocrates (c. 400 B.C.) mentions it and its virtues in his writings. The medicinal element of the herb is the rutinic acid produced by its stems and leaves. Many literary allusions are made to it, of which I quote the most notable:

"For you there's rosemary and rue; these keep
Seeming and savour all the winter long."
— *Winter's Tale*, SHAKESPEARE

"I'll set a bank of rue, sour herb of grace:
Rue, even for ruth . . ."
— *King Richard II*, SHAKESPEARE

"You must wear your rue with a difference."
— *Hamlet*, SHAKESPEARE

"To pull the thorn thy brow to braid,
And press the rue for wine."
— *Rokeby*, SIR WALTER SCOTT

"Then purged with euphrasy and rue
The visual nerve, for he had much to see."
— *Paradise Lost*, JOHN MILTON

Reeds and Grasses

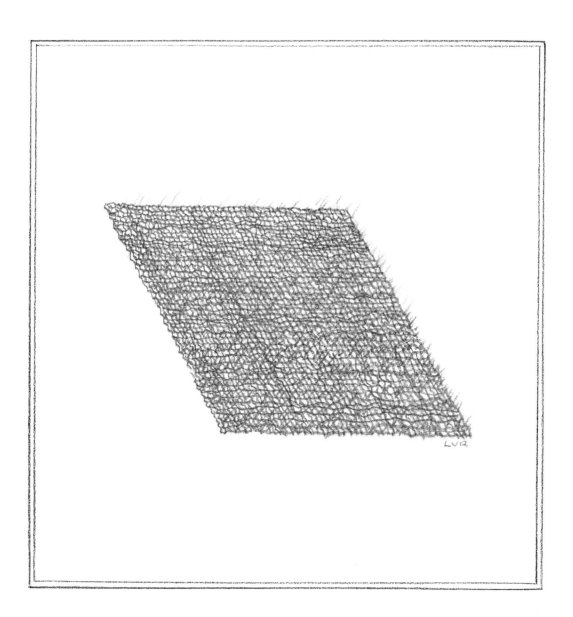

PLATE 40

HARASSED WEED

lana hebridica

If your LAWN (a cousin of FLAX) shows signs of wear, then spots and mildew, there is only one answer: replace it with HARASSED WEED. As is indicated by its botanical classification, this weed grass is native to the Hebrides where it has been developed, cultured and cultivated for centuries. It can be purchased in long rolls, then cut, trimmed and shaped to cover any surface. It is closely matted and is obtainable in a variety of hues. This makes it possible to have a basic color scheme established for your garden. It thrives in damp and foggy climates and its wearing qualities are legendary. I have some HARASSED WEED that I bought over twenty-five years ago that is still as good as new. It is so dense in its interwoven tendrils that no other vegetation can come through. It is far superior to the North American HOLM's PUN (*annominatio lusus verborum*) that thrives on the lowest form of humus. This latter should only be used in carefully selected spots and with great discretion.

LVR.

PLATE 41

HUATL

calamus azteca

HUATL is an Aztec word meaning huatl, pronounced huatl. It is a tall decorative marsh weed native to Lake Texcoco that surrounded the ancient Tenochtitlán, now Mexico City. The natives used its long leaves to weave mats of all sizes, called petatls. They are very durable if the leaves have been properly dried. The flower stems, usually crowned with a feathery top, dry out to an almost bamboo-like toughness and are interwoven to form walls and partitions in native huts. In the higher and cooler altitudes these partitions are often daubed with adobe, and the young shoots are often chopped up and used as a bond in the making of adobe bricks. In the temperate zones they are annuals and can be used as an interesting plant on the edge of a lake or pond. It's the perfect answer to what to do with that muddy spot.

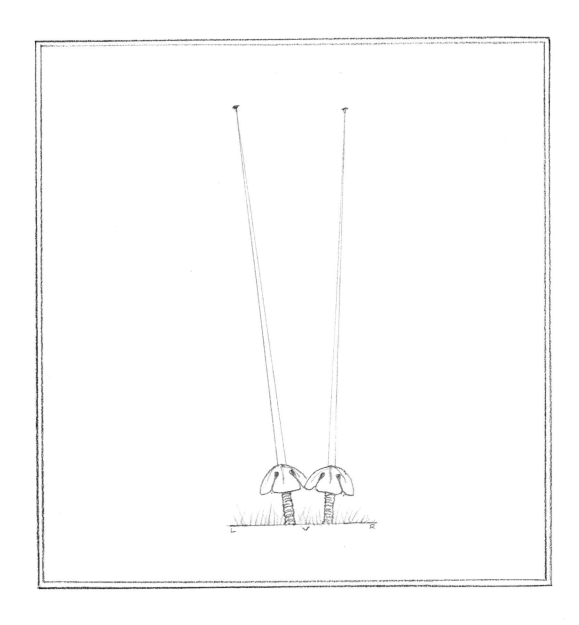

PLATE 42

DUALFOIL

chalybs frigidus

A DUALFOIL seed produces a few simple, flat leaves from the center of which spring twin spikes, often reaching a length of 3'-0" or more. They are interesting because of their varying cross sections and their steel-grey coloring. The tips of the spikes are extremely sharp and should be corked or "buttoned" to prevent any accidental but sometimes quite serious punctures to the careless gardener. Tempered by the hot sun and cooling summer rains, the spikes can be dried and used for indoor winter arrangements. Their strength and pliability make them ideal for fencing-in a small area of the garden. Just let them penetrate at intervals to the desired depth, and there you are. They are an adequate defence against the invasion of predators. Singularly secure from insect pests, they are subject to rust. Simple protective measures are enough to overcome this difficulty. They are valued for their color contrast and verticality in garden composition.

PLATE 43

SHEPHERD'S HAY

tripadium bucolicum

My home overlooks a meadow bordering Stage Harbor. It is separated from my garden by a fence used to keep the rabbits out and me in. I have left the meadow in its natural state and I find great joy in the measured procession of Beach Plum blossoms, daisies, butterfly weed, Queen Anne's lace, to the final glory of the wild asters, against a background of bayberry and the sea beyond. The whole is carpeted with a series of wild grasses that come up, bear their seed heads, then die down for the next variety to take over. I always look forward to the arrival of SHEPHERD'S HAY. Its bright green fronds and crook-like seed stems, swaying and dancing with the slightest breeze, bring gaiety and the sound of rustling laughter to my meadow and joy to my heart. My murmured "merci" to the Almighty falls like the gentle rain upon the place beneath.

PLATE 44

LONGBOTHAM'S GONTA SEED
arslonga vitabrevis

The introduction of the GONTA SEED to New England is attributed to a Salem sea captain, Erasmus Gaylord Longbotham, for many years engaged in the China trade. He brought the GONTA SEED from a small island off the China coast appropriately called Gonta. Brevity, they say, is the soul of wit and that makes GONTA SEED a very funny grass. It sprouts, grows, blooms and seeds all within the space of four days — what we used to call a split-week engagement on the road, in show business. Nevertheless, its bright green leaves and white flowers can make quite a showing. Certainly it is a greater contribution to our natural scene than the English sparrow, which was brought to America by one of Captain Longbotham's relatives by marriage, Charles Darwin Gaylord. All of which explains the sparrow's partiality to GONTA SEED. It's all in the family, so to speak. Since brevity is the soul of wit, GONTA SEED needs no mot.

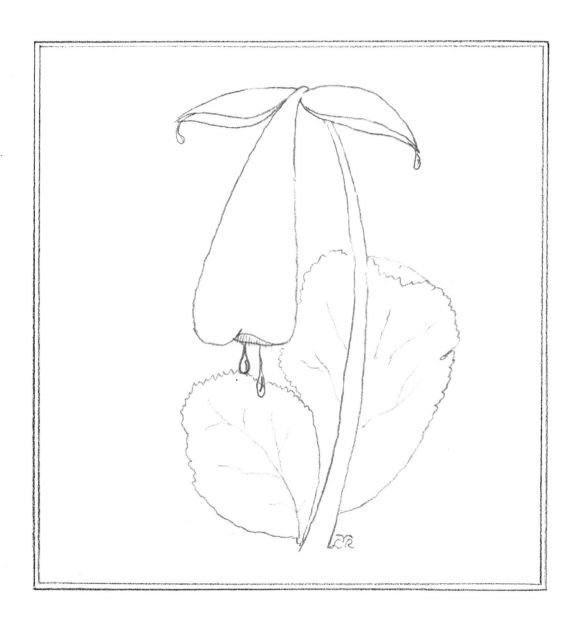

PLATE 45

DRIPPING NOSTRIL or COMMON COLD

nares pluviosae

Most gardeners are plagued with this plant at one time or another. Despite much research, horticulturists have discovered very little about it. Its sprays of green leaves and trumpet-like red flowers, continually dripping a noxious serum, make it an outstanding curiosity. It likes to keep its feet wet, but it can be eliminated by overwatering with an aspirin solution. My only advice is to stay home and enjoy it, while you can.

Noxious and Poisonous Plants and Vines

NOTE

It is not due to a psychopathic morbidity that I include this collection of Flora in this pamphlet, but because poisonous plants have found acceptance by so many gardeners. Oleanders, Angel Trumpet (a cultivated Jimson Weed) and Foxglove are all deadly but are also widely grown. Foxglove or Belladonna is used medicinally by ophthalmologists; drops used in the eyes distend the iris and make examination easier. At the turn of the century it was used cosmetically by certain ladies to give greater depth to their eyes, sacrificing their sight on the altar of beauty. A. Merritt, American toxicologist and science-fiction writer, pre-eminent in both careers, devoted his backyard in New York entirely to the cultivation of a poisonous plant garden. Therefore I do not feel it out of place to note down some unfamiliar varieties with a skull and crossbones appended. I forget whether it was Marshal Joffre or Pétain who said, "L'audace, toujours l'audace," but I say, "L'audace, but with caution," to mix a metaphor.

PLATE 46

TEMPTATION or ST. ANTHONY'S BANE
rhus sempiternus

TEMPTATION belongs to the poison ivy, poison oak and poison sumac family. Often mentioned in the Bible, it is first found in Genesis, growing in the Garden of Eden. Some biblical scholars of the Apocrypha even claim that it twined around the trunk of the tree of knowledge of good and evil. TEMPTATION has been with us ever since, springing spontaneously in the most unexpected places. Indeed, man's fear of it is expressed in the Lord's prayer, "and lead us not into temptation . . ." Its poison is insidious and virulent, at first causing an almost unbearable itch, then leading to physical and psychoneurotic complications of every sort and variety. Its attractive trifoliate leaves and seed pods, shaped like a beckoning finger, have trapped many a hapless gardener. There are some hardy souls, who have overcome the common allergy, who can uproot it with their bare hands, and the roots are long and deep. The cultivation of VIRTUE (q.v.) is perhaps the best defense against this universal enemy of mankind.

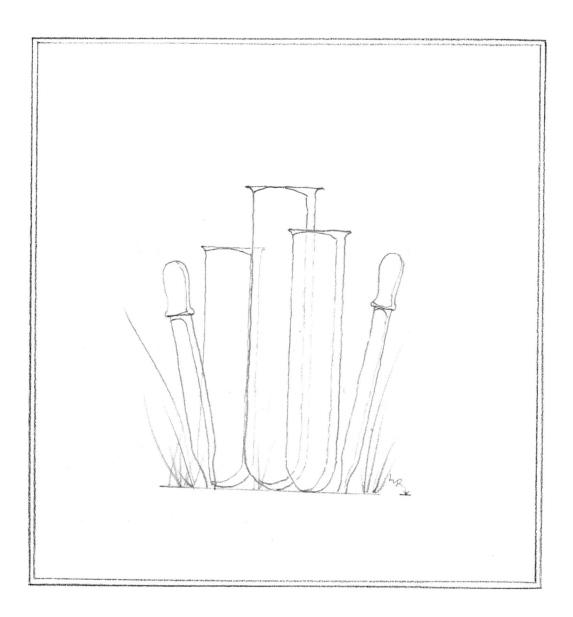

PLATE 47

SWEET PEE

morbus senilis

The SWEET PEE is a fungus proliferated by wind-borne spores and germinating wherever it finds favorable conditions. These conditions, however, are unfavorable to the gardener, as they indicate an organic, chemical imbalance. An expert should be consulted immediately, to suggest what treatment to use. Sometimes a simple adjustment of plant food will alleviate the condition. If, however, the situation is ignored and inadequate tests are made, the situation may be aggravated. Positive proof is the appearance of either DIABETES (*saccharum abundans*) or HYPOGLYCEMIA (*saccharum imperfectus*). These are highly virulent, poisonous fungi. The gardener is then doomed to keep his property permanently sprayed with Langerhans solution, basically insulin. In the Middle Ages the accepted procedure was a novena to St. Pancreas. It may still work, but it takes an unshakable faith.

PLATE 48

MUMPS

glandula tumida

The first notes and classification of MUMPS is attributed to Carl von Linné, better known as Linnaeus, who devised the modern method of plant classification (1707–1778). He wrote over 180 books on the subject. The second and perhaps more accurate classification is attributed to America's leading botanist and friend of Charles Darwin, Asa Gray (1810–1888). Unlike the Sweet Pee, which usually appears in old gardens, as its Latin classification implies, although it may appear in new gardens just as well, MUMPS is common to newly tilled ground, although it may appear in well-established gardens, where its infection is more serious and can result in permanent damage. It has a characteristic bi-globular blossom, which lasts about two weeks, and then dies down completely. Recurrence is rare. It should be left strictly alone and undisturbed and be sure to keep children away from it. This reddish flower seems to appear spontaneously, but its growth is due to contagion from a neighboring garden, the seeds either wind-borne or dropped by birds. It can give you a swell time while you have it.

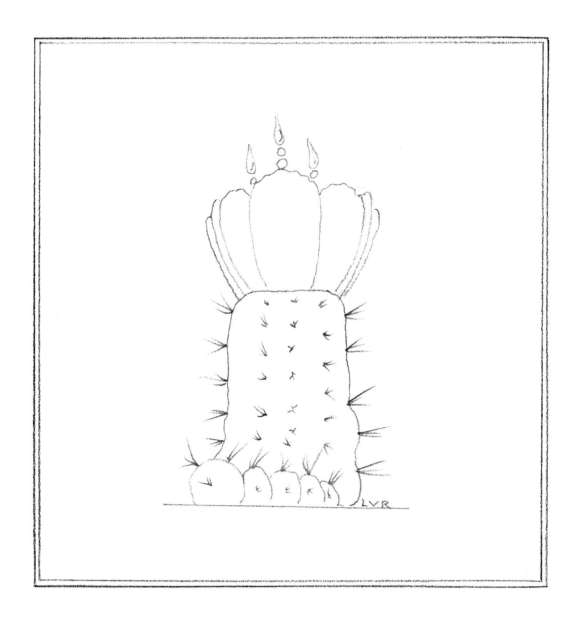

PLATE 49

HYDROPHILIA or DROPSY

oedema anasarca

HYDROPHILIA is the botanical antithesis of HYDROPHOBIA (*timor aquosus*). A cactus, it is smooth-skinned, thorny and pulpy. It is filled to the bursting point with an aqueous fluid in the main body of the plant, as well as in the minor shoots growing out of its base. This condition is attributed to a faulty capillary development. It is very painful to the touch. Its blossoms are red and purulent, also very rare except in old infestations. Long-suffering growers call it their ACHYLLOUS HEEL.

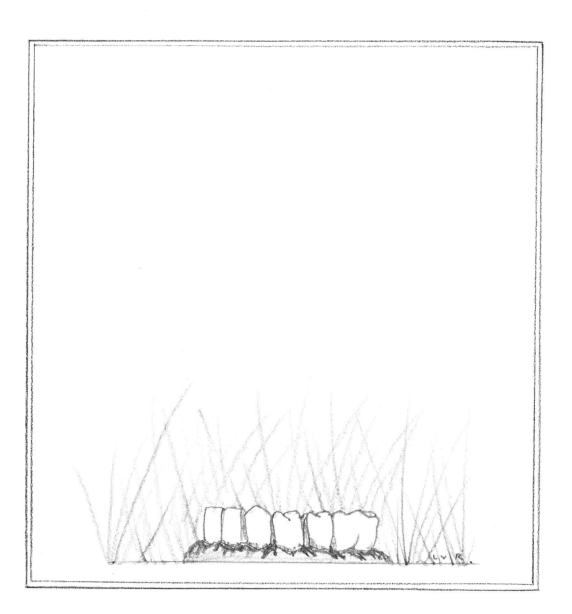

PLATE 50

BLEEDING GUM

pyorrhea vulgaris

BLEEDING GUM is a denticulated white or light yellow fungus growing out of a red base. It exudes a red serum and generally has an unpleasant odor. Professional care and treatment are essential to its eradication. To ignore it is merely asking for real trouble. A solution made from Blue Gentian is one of the specifics recommended.

PLATE 51

FLOTSAM, JETSAM and LIGAM

sordes maritimus

I have grouped these seashore plants together because of their great similarity. LIGAM can be distinguished from the others by its identifying markings. Some collectors of botanical specimens prize a variety of FLOTSAM and JETSAM called DRIFTWOOD (*lignum aestus maris*), for its variegated shapes and texture. It is rich in chemical content and burns, by consequence, with a motley flame.

PLATE 52

RED HOT DOGMA

credo communista

This highly controversial plant, resembling a miniature cattail, is first recorded in History as a vital part of Inca culture and civilization. Its popularity had a revival in France in the late eighteenth century, but events soon headed it off. Some intellectuals who took an interest in it during the nineteenth century recognized its identifying marx. It appeared sporadically until 1917 when it took root in Russia where it enjoys a tremendous popularity, surpassed today by its wide dissemination in China. In the United States it has had a vehement but limited popularity. American gardeners seem to prefer a plant of ancient Greek origin, established in colonial gardens toward the end of the eighteenth century, called DEMOCRACY (*vox populi*), despite the time and care it requires and the fact that it is at times unwieldy.

PLATE 53

HEARTBURN

ira digestiva

HEARTBURN is one of the bitter herbs, like Hyssop and Rue. The acrid taste of its foliage, the burning red and orange of its blooms, distinguish it beyond reasonable doubt. Most gardeners do not care for it, in fact they avoid its culture as much as possible. Any flourishing specimen of HEARTBURN indicates an acute acid condition and the generous use of a lime solution will definitely discourage it. The ingestion of HEARTBURN will cause acute digestive discomfort, but it can hardly be termed lethal.

PLATE 54

DEADLY LAMPSHADE

lux vomica

Perhaps no other flower has been hybridized into so many shapes, colors and textures as the DEADLY LAMPSHADE. In color it encompasses the entire range of known hues and tints; some specimens are multicolored in interesting patterns. The petals may be of a silken softness, parchment-like or even crystalline. A hardy perennial, it is indispensable in interior decoration and may also be used outdoors. Its lethal qualities are not found in the bloom itself, but in the stem and root system, which may be quite extensive. Direct contact with it will produce anything from a mild case of shock to complete annihilation. The plant should be handled with extreme caution and wariness, but there is no doubt that its use is invaluable in brightening up its surroundings. Close association with the DEADLY LAMPSHADE can be an illuminating experience. Many scientifically inclined amateurs and professionals, since the days of Benjamin Franklin, have tried to establish its relationship to the direct and alternating CURRANT (*fons lucidus*), with great intensity and some success.

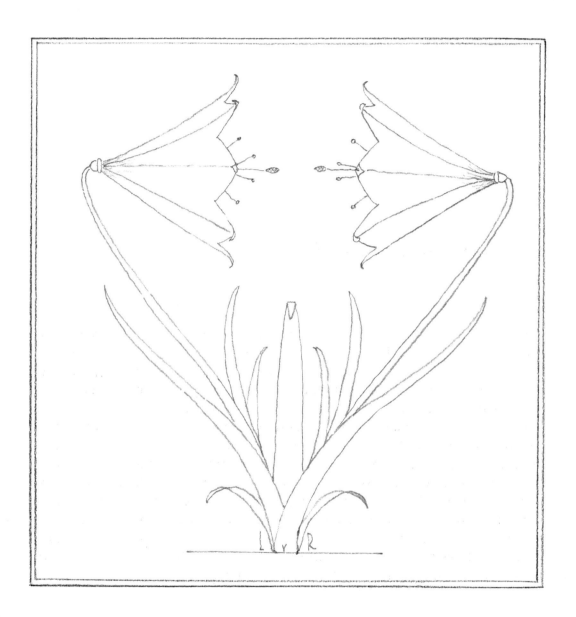

PLATE 55

VIRTUE

suumipsius praemium

It would not be sportsmanlike on my part to catalog a collection of noxious and poisonous plants without appending a panacea or antidote. Hence, VIRTUE. The seeds of VIRTUE must be deeply imbedded and, once they have sprouted, the plants need continual attention and care. You will be rewarded with lily-like blooms of great purity, exhaling a heavy scent often referred to as "the odor of sanctity." VIRTUE can be cultivated by almost anyone, but it is a must in cloister gardens, where you can see some magnificent displays. It exudes a volatile oil that neutralizes the exhalations of TEMPTATION (q.v.). Its deep root system also attacks and chokes the roots of all evil plants. I once heard Frank Kiernan, humorist and naturalist, say, "I served four years in the army in World War I and I never hurt anybody." The same can be said of VIRTUE. By all means, avoid specimens of EASY VIRTUE (*mulier lascivia*). They can be highly infectious.

The Malignant Parasite

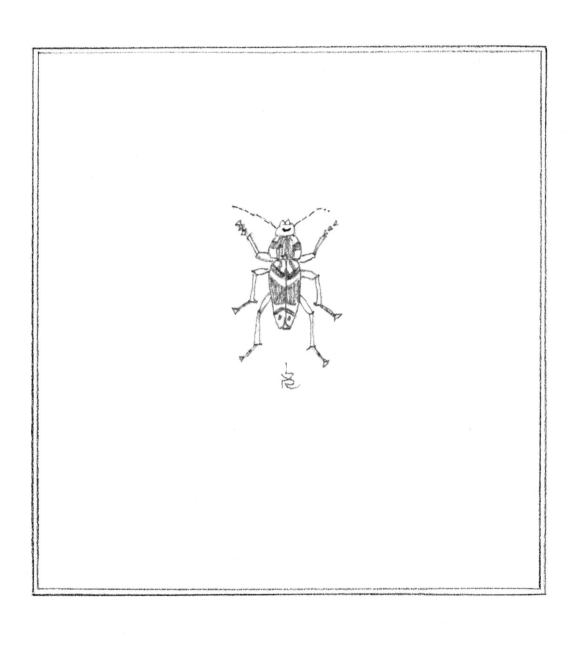

PLATE 56

SPEEKNO WEEVIL
demortuis nilnisibonum

Charles Darwin (1809–1882), on his famous expedition on the *Beagle*, first noticed this insect on an uncharted coral atoll in the South Pacific, probably because there was nothing else to be noted there. He named it the "SPEEKNO WEEVIL" after the native name of the islet. To his surprise he found it prevalent everywhere he went, even in England. The nasty little scarab had been under his nose all the time. Darwin felt it was too common to mention in his *Journal of a Naturalist*. He did mention it in great detail in a letter to his American friend, the botanist Asa Gray. He explained his classification "demortuis," saying that he found many similarities between SPEEKNO WEEVIL and the deathwatch beetle. This letter has been lost so all we know is pure hearsay. French botanists, on the other hand, feel that it is neither a weevil nor a beetle, but a tick. They have isolated two varieties, the *douloureux* and the *nerveux*. The first, in mild infestation, will respond to the application of a formula obtainable at any chemist's. Serious infestations may require drastic extirpation. The second may respond to analysis and therapy, but it may be necessary to tie-off or cut the affected parts. In either case professional consultation and help is mandatory.

The SPEEKNO WEEVIL is a crashing borer, laying its eggs under the bark of woody shrubs. When hatched the larvae feed on their nest. Their bite is worse than their bark.

The SPEEKNO WEEVIL, like the horseshoe crab and the wood louse, is a rare prehistoric life form, virtually unchanged. Man first became acquainted with it when the pithecanthropus decided to become erectus.

EPILOGUE

Many of my readers (if I have any) will be convinced that these botanical species I have herein described do not exist, that they are pure figments of my imagination and that I am pulling their legumes. I can only reply that many seed and garden catalogs will list a variety of Garden Balsam, the SULTANI IMPATIENS, but seldom illustrate it. To those Latinists who will quibble over the genus classifications, I can only apologize humbly. I hope sincerely that those who leaf through these pages will find as much enjoyment in them as I did in collating them.

THE END

terminus ultimus

No comment.